# WHERE'S WALLY?
# MONSTER HUNT

## MARTIN HANDFORD

WALKER BOOKS
AND SUBSIDIARIES

LONDON • BOSTON • SYDNEY • AUCKLAND

# GRRR WALLY-WATCHERS!

WATCH OUT, THERE ARE MONSTERS ABOUT! HUNT HIGH AND LOW FOR THE FRIENDLIEST TO THE MOST FEROCIOUS CREATURES THAT ARE LURKING IN STRANGE PLACES, WAITING TO POUNCE! DODGE STINKY SWAMP BEASTS, DIVE WITH DEEP SEA MONSTERS AND SCREAM WITH HOWLING SPOOKS. HAVE A FIERCELY FUN TIME WITH ALIENS, DRAGONS AND MY DINOSAUR PALS, TOO.

LOOK OUT FOR ME AND THERE ARE MANY MORE MONSTROUSLY GOOD THINGS TO SEARCH FOR AS WELL.

YOU MUST ALSO FIND THIS ESSENTIAL CAN OF MONSTER FOOD TO TEMPT BEASTLY TASTE BUDS BEFORE WE'RE DINNER!

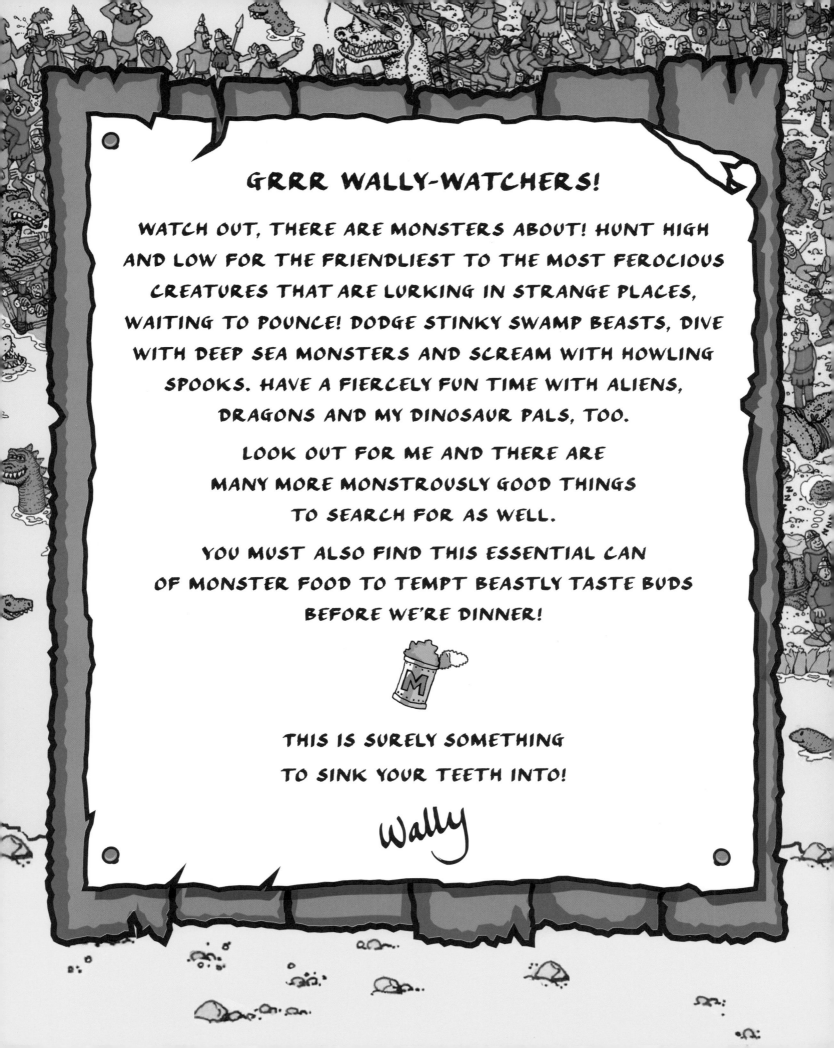

THIS IS SURELY SOMETHING TO SINK YOUR TEETH INTO!

*Wally*

# THE GRRR-EAT ESCAPE

Follow the trail to make it through this land
of mighty monsters. Beware as they may bite!

❶ **Start** at the blue monster causing mayhem at the dam. Quickly jump over the top of the dam and meet the two monsters in love. ❷ **Join** the hunters pulling the patched monster's tail then turn around and slither along the pink snake. ❸ **Pass** the artist and hop across the channel, dodging the enormous

monster standing up on its hind legs. ❹ **Pull** on a spiky disguise then follow the hungry monsters to rescue the man underneath the triangle. ❺ **Swim** across the channel and climb onto the raft. ❻ **Creep** by the snoozing monster, passing the marooned figure sitting on an island. ❼ **Closely** follow the bank of the river, stepping over the tail of the red monster by the bridge. ❽ **Keep** going until you reach the giant water snake with an exceedingly long tongue. ❾ **Finally,** slide down the pink monster and join in the fun at the playground.

Top monster-shirking marks – you made it!

# MONSTER ATTACK

Splash, splat, splurge! Colour in this monstrous lighthouse scene and make the gooey monster gunge as gross as possible!

**MORE THINGS TO FIND**
- [ ] A dragon wearing goggles
- [ ] Seven ladders
- [ ] A dragon flying upside-down
- [ ] A gloopy spiral
- [ ] A sleeping dragon

# FLIP FLOP SILHOUETTES

Sit opposite a friend, so you both have a scene facing you. See who can match the silhouettes from their logbook to their scene first – but beware, only four silhouettes appear in each scene!

# MONSTROUS MEDDLING

Something has got its claws into this picture and muddled it up. Can you draw it correctly in the grid below?

**MORE THINGS TO FIND**
Can you find the fiery-red flying dare-devil on this page somewhere else in this book?

# RIDDLE-O-SAURUS

Read the ridiculous riddles and match them to the pictures.

ANNIE ANKYLOSAURUS IS A BRILLIANT BATTER.

SPIKE STYRACOSAURUS OFFERS A SPEEDY RIDE.

PENELOPE LIKES TO PERFECT HER PREHISTORIC POM-POMS.

TOT UP OUR TERRIFIC TOTAL TO MAKE 128.

CASEY GIVES CAREY A ROCKY KNOCK.

# HOWLING HUNTING

There's nothing Odlaw likes more than prowling around in the dark and sneaking up on scary spooks and spectres. Can you find these things he's spotted in this creepy castle?

## ODLAW'S I-SPY!

- Two witches flying backwards
- A witch flying upside-down
- A dancing Frankenstein's monster
- A vampire holding a teddy bear
- A ghost train
- A ghost scaring a vampire
- A broom riding a witch
- A gargoyle with a very long tongue
- A vampire holding a bat

✎ Write your own checklist below of monstery things to find in the world around you! Here are a few ideas to get you started:

☐ A creature with big paws
☐ A monster truck
☐ A statue pulling a face

☐ .................................................
☐ .................................................
☐ .................................................
☐ .................................................
☐ .................................................

# SWAMPY SWIRL

Read Odlaw's swampy, swirly message by turning the page in an anti-clockwise direction. Watch out, the message is written backwards!

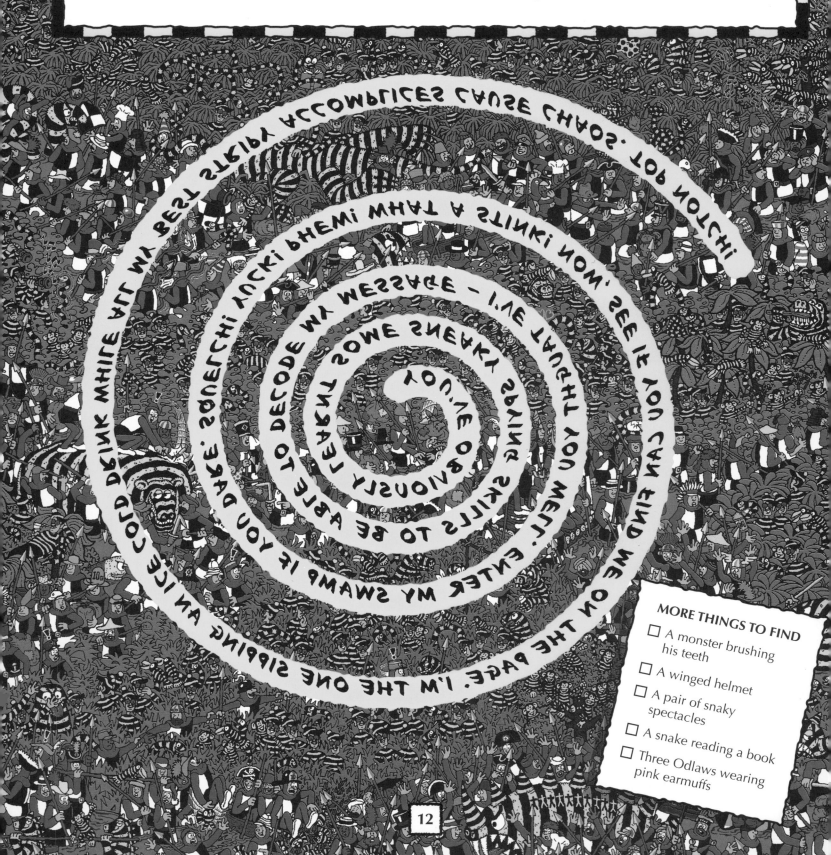

**MORE THINGS TO FIND**

☐ A monster brushing his teeth

☐ A winged helmet

☐ A pair of snaky spectacles

☐ A snake reading a book

☐ Three Odlaws wearing pink earmuffs

# CONNECT THE BONES

Can you join up all nine bones by using only four lines?
You must not lift your pen off the page, but your
lines can go outside of the grid.

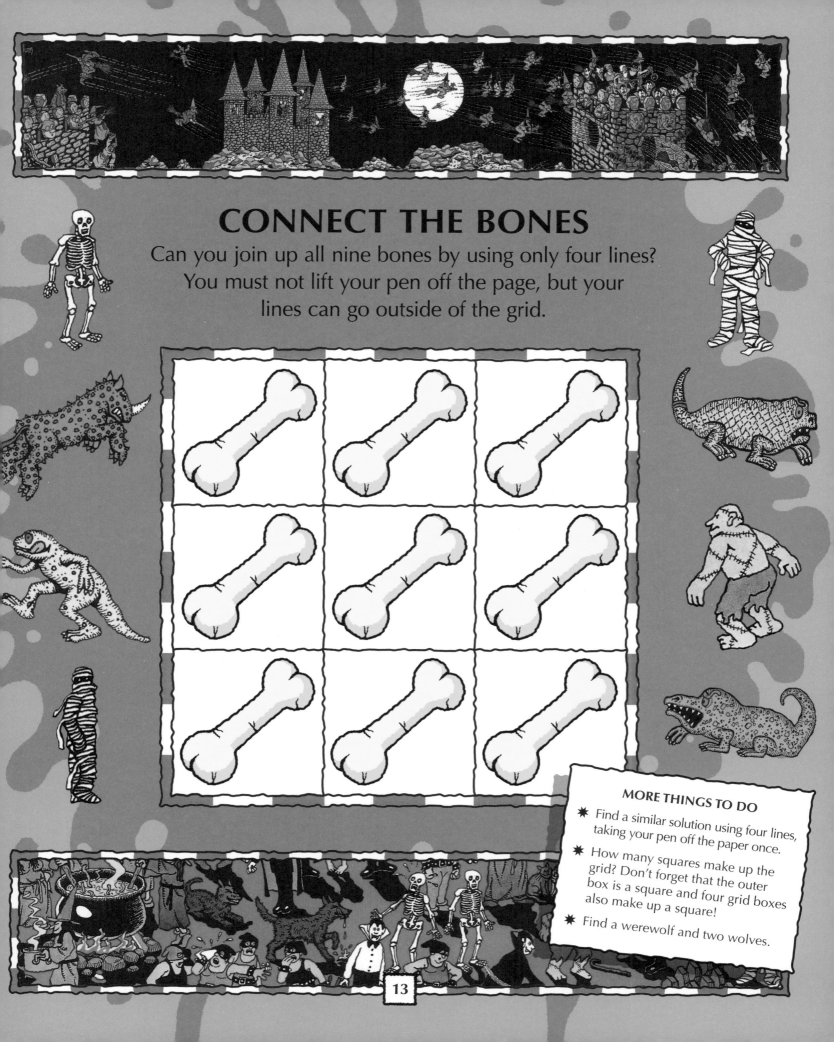

## MORE THINGS TO DO

✳ Find a similar solution using four lines, taking your pen off the paper once.

✳ How many squares make up the grid? Don't forget that the outer box is a square and four grid boxes also make up a square!

✳ Find a werewolf and two wolves.

# BEASTLY ART

Unleash your creativity and fill these frames with beastly art of your own.

# EXTRA TERRESTRIAL TERRORS!

Finish drawing these galactic aliens and colour them in.
Have fun adding extra eyes, noses, ears and terrifying teeth.
Create some rockets zooming among the stars, too!

# LOST FOR WORDS

Look for the names of ten troublesome monsters
lurking in this wordsearch.

VAMPIRE
DRAGON
OGRE
MINOTAUR
WEREWOLF

GRIFFIN
ZOMBIE
ALIEN
BIGFOOT
GOBLIN
KRAKEN

E W M C R W A L
I R D I L O E M R I E
M P N R N E K R A K E N T
V A L C A O G R E E S U O J
J R L M G T L A W N Z G F T E
N I O O A E Z O M B I E P E
L B N U R T L V L K C
O G R I F F I N R

**MORE THINGS TO FIND**

☐ A bat flying upside-down

☐ Two smiling ghosts

☐ A yellow alien monster

# DRAGON DELIGHT

Draw lots of winged, fire-breathing contestants to join in this dare-devil dragon flying competition!

## MORE THINGS TO DO

Choose your favourite dragon (it might be one that you have drawn) and give it a name. What do you think its eggs look like and what is its favourite food?

Look at the picture and find:

☐ A dragon with a very long tail

☐ A dragon egg

☐ A red spotty bag on a stick

# DOTTY DOT-TO-DOT

Join up the numbered red dots to reveal the last contestant competing for the flying competition crown!

**MORE THINGS TO FIND**
- ☐ A person upside-down
- ☐ A man with a very long beard
- ☐ A dragon wearing a bandana

# NUMBER CRUNCHING

Solve the number puzzle to help Woof jump down through the clouds.
Subtract 1 from any red number and add 1 to any blue number. Then draw a
path to the finish by connecting up eleven clouds which add up to the number 5.

Start

Finish

**MORE THINGS TO DO**
* Find a monster with a yellow spot
* Find a monster with a gap tooth
* Which cloud has the highest final total?

20

# WINGED WONDERS

Spot ten differences between these two scenes from the Land of Dragon Flyers.

# FEARSOME FIEND

Create the most ferocious, snarling, warty beast that you can imagine in the middle of this scene.

**MORE THINGS TO DO**
* Draw a crest on the white shield
* Find a fleeing glove
* Colour in the white plume
* Spot a dinosaur!

WOW, OUR MIGHTY MONSTER HUNT WAS A ROARING SUCCESS! DID YOU HAVE A FAVOURITE BEASTLY ENCOUNTER? I HOPE YOU REMEMBERED TO FIND THE CAN OF MONSTER FOOD, TO KEEP THE GNASHING NASTIES AT BAY? IF NOT, YOU'LL NEED TO RETRACE YOUR STEPS THROUGH OUR TREACHEROUS QUEST.

OH, AND CAN YOU SPOT THIS SWAMP-DWELLING LIZARD HIDING IN ONE OF THE SCENES?

GRRR-BYE!

Wally

The monster hunt isn't over yet! Cautiously flip back through the pages of this book and find these curious things in the stripy shapes and checklist.

## CHECKLIST

- An alien wearing a red skirt
- Three seahorses
- A beastly stepping-stone
- Three lobsters in a bed
- A broom fight
- A sea-lion
- A dog, cat and mouse chase
- A monster blackboard
- A bone wicket
- Three witches riding one broomstick
- A figure fleeing a shield
- A person wearing a chicken costume

# HERE ARE SOME ANSWERS TO THE HARDEST PUZZLES. DON'T GIVE UP ON THE OTHERS – WHY NOT ASK YOUR FRIENDS TO HELP?

## P. 9 RIDDLE-O-SAURUS

1. Tot up our terrific total to make 128.
2. Penelope likes to perfect her prehistoric pom-poms.
3. Casey gives Carey a rocky knock.
4. Spike Styracosaurus offers a speedy ride.
5. Annie Ankylosaurus is a brilliant batter.

## P. 12 SWAMPY SWIRL

You've obviously learnt some sneaky spying skills to be able to decode my message – I've taught you well. Enter my swamp if you dare. Squelch! Yuck! Phew! What a stink! Now, see if you can find me on the page. I'm the one sipping an ice cold drink while all my best stripy accomplices cause chaos. Top notch!

## P. 13 CONNECT THE BONES

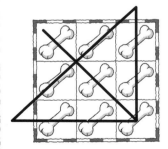

MORE THINGS TO DO

14 squares make up the grid

## P. 17 LOST FOR WORDS

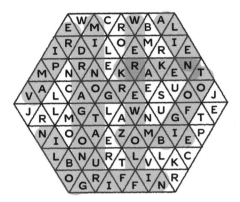

## P. 20 NUMBER CRUNCHING

First published 2023 by Walker Books Ltd, 87 Vauxhall Walk, London SE11 5HJ • 10 9 8 7 6 5 4 3 2 1 © 1987–2023 Martin Handford • The right of Martin Handford to be identified as author/illustrator of this work has been asserted in accordance with the Copyright, Designs and Patents Act 1988. • This book has been typeset in Wallyfont and Optima • Printed in China • All rights reserved. • No part of this book may be reproduced, transmitted or stored in an information retrieval system in any form or by any means, graphic, electronic or mechanical, including photocopying, taping and recording, without prior written permission from the publisher. • British Library Cataloguing in Publication Data: a catalogue record for this book is available from the British Library. • ISBN 978-1-5295-0737-9 www.walker.co.uk